Little RIDDLERS

Warwickshire

Edited By Daisy Job

First published in Great Britain in 2018 by:

 Young**Writers**

Young Writers
Remus House
Coltsfoot Drive
Peterborough
PE2 9BF
Telephone: 01733 890066
Website: www.youngwriters.co.uk

FOREWORD

Dear Reader,
Are you ready to get your thinking caps on to puzzle
your way through this wonderful collection?

Young Writers' Little Riddlers competition set out to
encourage young writers to create their own riddles.
Their answers could be whatever or whoever their
imaginations desired; from people to places, animals
to objects, food to seasons. Riddles are a great way
to further the children's use of poetic expression,
including onomatopoeia and similes, as well as
encourage them to 'think outside the box' by
providing clues without giving the answer away
immediately.

All of us here at Young Writers believe in the
importance of inspiring young children to produce
creative writing, including poetry, and we feel that
seeing their own riddles in print will keep that
creative spirit burning brightly and proudly.

We hope you enjoy riddling your way through this
book as much as we enjoyed reading all the entries.

CONTENTS

Emilia Butler (6)	55
Emily Harper (5)	56
Millie Clarke (5)	57
Eleanor Basnett (5)	58
Amelia Moon (5)	59
Miriam Jouni (6)	60
William Harker (6)	61
Hope Poole (5)	62
Reece Robson (5)	63

St Francis Catholic Primary School, Bedworth

Nyah Habinshuti (7)	64
Jem Luca Raggett (7)	65
Olivia Simmons (6)	66
Oliver Gilbey (6)	67
James Charlton-Horrillo (6)	68
Holly Garratt (7)	69
Ethan Coyle (7)	70
Dominic Charlton-Horrillo (6)	71
Mailey Grace Golby (7)	72
Isabella Campbell (7)	73
Miley Green (6)	74
Lily Jade Spencer (7)	75
Leon Max Sumner (6)	76
Lydia Crowley (6)	77
Sarah Murphy (6)	78
Scarlett Dadley (6)	79
Joshua McAnespie (7)	80
Thomas Dixon (7)	81
Freddie Bayliss (6)	82
Cian Kincaid (7)	83
Oscar Leszek Wilk (6)	84
Olivia Katherine Jones (7)	85
Louisa Thorpe (7)	86
Iga Laura Surys (7)	87
Liam Gilbody (6)	88

St Mary's Catholic Primary School, Southam

Florence Isla Forgan (6)	89
Lydia Reeves (7)	90
Elena Raiseborough (7)	91
Gwendolyn Bosworth (6)	92
Sophie Bartlett (6)	93
Carolina Ferreira Jorge (7)	94
Maya Gulliver (7)	95
Olivia Mulkeirins (6)	96
Ada Sztuka (6)	97
Lyekka Mae Robinson (5)	98
Jacob Leslie Holden (6)	99
Logan Crowther (6)	100
Sofia Reeves (5)	101

The Revel CE Primary School, Monks Kirby

Rosa Sinclair (7)	102
Krystal Brook Hipwell (6)	103
Katherine Harrison (6)	104
Philippa Bennett (7)	105
Annie Zhou (5)	106
Charlie Main (7)	107
Poppy Rose Lindstrom (7)	108
Lauchlan MacKenzie (6)	109
Sasha Pickering (6)	110
Phoebe Bloor (5)	111
Eloise Smith (6)	112
Lydia Wallwin (6)	113
Adam Lea (6)	114
Vinnie Humphreys (5)	115
James Burton (5)	116
Myles Wright (5)	117
Oliver Mann (6)	118
Isabel Rees (6)	119
Sinead Naylor (6)	120
Eira Pitham (6)	121
Jacob Farr (6)	122
Amelia Price (7)	123
Adley Ball (5)	124
Millie Jones (7)	125

Lara Grieves-Smith (6)	126	
Arthur Wang (7)	127	
Maddie Jankowski (6)	128	

Welford-On-Avon Primary School, Welford On Avon

Lara Grieves-Smith (6)	126
Arthur Wang (7)	127
Maddie Jankowski (6)	128
Lottie-Anne Cardwell (5)	129
Stanley Smith (6)	130
Taylor Smith (5)	131
Alfie Dennis Wright (5)	132
Evie Sawyer (6)	133
Tilda Passemard (7)	134
Edward Barrett-Leafe (7)	135
Dominic Poole (6)	136
Layla Jade Huddlestone (7)	137
Lily Grace Elliot (7)	138
Gia Murphy (6)	139
Charlie Johnson (7)	140
Elsie Sorren Gleed (5)	141
Darcy Victoria Forinton (6)	142
Chloe Isobel Porcas (6)	143
Edward Town (5)	144
Ethan William Richardson (7)	145
Douglas George Harrison (7)	146
Leo Hunt (6)	147
Harris Leech (5)	148
Autumn Rose Morris (6)	149
Leeson Lee Tolin (6)	150
James Thomas Dew (6)	151
Keira Pargetter (7)	152
Ella Louise Irons (7)	153
Bradley Mackley (7)	154
Elsie May Ascroft (6)	155
Emily Carol Green (6)	156
Maisy Mia Masterson (7)	157
Alfie Green (6)	158
Ryan James Fox (6)	159
Reuben Oliver Wells (5)	160
Lydia Tomlin (6)	161
April Steele (5)	162
Amelie Pickering (6)	163
Nanci Fellows (7)	164
Elizabeth Barnett (5)	165
Taylah Bottomley (7)	166

Welford-On-Avon Primary School, Welford On Avon

William Allan (7)	167
Harry Millwood (7)	168
Benji Fernandez (7)	170
Luke Mulliner (7)	171
Abigail Twigg (7)	172
Olivia Flack (7)	173
Katie Potter (6)	174
Oscar Farnell (6)	175
Aiden Kesic (6)	176
Daisy Unsworth (7)	177
Emily McCarthy (6)	178
Ben George Alderman (6)	179
Dylan Warren (7)	180
Sam Bright (5)	181
Ines Aughey (6)	182
Elizabeth Davies (5)	183
Bethany Hills (5)	184
Pixie-Blue Purtill (6)	185
Tom Yates (5)	186
Archie Eaton (6)	187
Ava Scott (6)	188
Jo Kowal (5)	189

THE POEMS

The Milk Maker

Hey diddle diddle
I live on Old MacDonald's farm.
I can be black and white.
Bigger than a mouse
But smaller than an elephant.
I like to eat grass that is nice and green.
With each chew I say moo.
What am I?

Answer: A cow.

Olivia Coton (7)

What Am I?

I am a good flyer
A fancy hitter
A destructive pounder
An excellent hunter
What am I?

Answer: Pokémon.

George Broughton (6)
Arnold Lodge School, Leamington Spa

What Am I?

The clouds are red.
It is big and hot.
No water can live here.
It is about two hundred metres.
There is no water.
There is lava rock.
The bombs drop to the floor.
What am I?

Answer: A volcano.

James Gonzalez Swinfield (6)
Arnold Lodge School, Leamington Spa

What Am I?

I am a stripy, small creature.
A little crawler.
A furry sniffer.
A forest shuffler.
A wild scratcher.
A fast runner.
A long-tailed biter.
What am I?

Answer: A raccoon.

Henry Bunting (6)
Arnold Lodge School, Leamington Spa

What Is It?

It's an animal
Dogs like chasing this animal.
It doesn't like rain.
It likes milk and it likes food.
It likes toys a lot.
What is it?

Answer: A cat.

Paige Keegan (6)
Arnold Lodge School, Leamington Spa

Who Am I?

I am an electric attacker.
A cute cuddler.
A ghost.
A fairy type.
An iron tail slapper.
A Pokémon player.
Who am I?

Answer: Mimikyu.

Niocol Slattery (7)
Arnold Lodge School, Leamington Spa

What Am I?

I sail across the sea.
I look for treasure.
I can be good or bad.
I scrub the deck.
I say, "Ahoy matey!"
What am I?

Answer: A pirate.

Aminah Chechi (6)
Arnold Lodge School, Leamington Spa

Fluffy Animal

I am fluffy.
I have long ears.
I am a mammal.
I move by jumping.
I am normally brown.
I have a white tail.
What am I?

Answer: A rabbit.

Charlotte Chater (6)
Arnold Lodge School, Leamington Spa

What Am I?

I am...
A slippery customer.
An ice brainer.
A top of my head curver.
A sweet taster.
A creamy melter.
What am I?

Answer: An ice lolly.

Thabisa Sibanda (6)
Arnold Lodge School, Leamington Spa

Floating On The Sea

It goes because of its fan.
It goes other places.
It is big.
It has a hook.
It floats on water.
What is it?

Answer: A ship.

Suvan Sahoo (6)

Arnold Lodge School, Leamington Spa

Rare Puncher, The Ninja

I am
A pretty rare puncher
A wave backer
A cat copier
Before a second evolver
A bomb forcer
What am I?

Answer: Riolu.

Suhjaan Hayer (6)
Arnold Lodge School, Leamington Spa

Flappy Flying

I can fly.
I am red.
I am a type of bird.
I like flying.
I eat worms.
I live in a tree.
What am I?

Answer: A robin.

Sriya Sreejith (6)
Arnold Lodge School, Leamington Spa

Fast Shot

It zooms like a cheetah.
It's very sharp.
It is used in war.
It is very dangerous.
What is it?

Answer: Bowmasters.

Brandon Mansfield (7)
Arnold Lodge School, Leamington Spa

Dinosaur

I am a fast runner
A high climber
A killer
An extinct hunter
A meat eater
What am I?

Answer: A dilophosaurus.

Michael Chater (7)
Arnold Lodge School, Leamington Spa

What Am I?

I am a fast pouncer.
A royal leader.
A terrifying roarer.
A furry fighter.
What am I?

Answer: A lion.

Tao Fenwick (8)
Arnold Lodge School, Leamington Spa

Who Am I?

I am a crazy shouter
A loud banger
A noisy jumper
A funny joker
Who am I?

Answer: My brother.

Safa Shah (6)
Arnold Lodge School, Leamington Spa

What Am I?

I am
A good melter
A brain freezer
A yummy tummy filler
What am I?

Answer: Ice cream.

Angel Leel (6)
Arnold Lodge School, Leamington Spa

Riddle School

I am amazingly short, the size of someone's ankle!

I'm a hero! I'm also very charming and amazingly likeable.

I'm sometimes crafty and not too tricky.

I am always a bit sly and mischievous.

I'm always speeding along the road.

Every time I sword fight, I fight angrily and confidently.

I'm ginger and yellow. I grin a lot!

I'm laughing nearly every day!

I have a master whose father died.

I have red sparkly boots and a green hat from my master.

I have a bag to catch animals and give them to the king.

Who am I?

Answer: Puss in Boots.

Luca King (7)

Brownsover Community School, Brownsover

Can You Guess Who I Am?

I am very beautiful and extremely kind.
I love helping people and animals.
I'm attractive, brave and bold.
I am very charming.
I am always smiling happily.
My character never gives up hope.
I think my mother is an old witch,
who is disguised.
I was stolen when I was a baby.
I was locked in a tower.
I am a lost princess.
I long to see the outside world.
My hair is long enough to climb.
Who am I?

Answer: Rapunzel.

Seth Baylis (6)
Brownsover Community School, Brownsover

Can You Guess Me?

I am incredibly tiny and cute.
If you are clever,
you might see me at night in shops.
I can be sneaky and cheeky,
but normally I am kind.
I like to sneak into the shoemaker's shop
and make unbelievably beautiful shoes
for him!
I wear extremely old rags
because I am very poor.
Helping others makes me fill with
happiness.
I am fearless when exploring the shops.
What am I?

Answer: An elf.

Teilo Carter (7)
Brownsover Community School, Brownsover

Guessed Me Yet?

I live with my mother and baby brother.
I have the prettiest dark brown hair ever!
I am a beautiful girl with a pink bow
and a stripy shirt.
I am a bit cheeky and extremely kind.
A wolf grinned at me
when I was in the woods.
I was taking food to my granny.
My granny looked strange!
I have a bright red cape
that my granny made for me.
Who am I?

Answer: Little Red Riding Hood.

Amy Barnes (6)
Brownsover Community School, Brownsover

Can You Solve My Riddle?

I'm short and extremely fluffy.
I have two horns
And one tiny, pink glistening nose.
I have one mini fluffy tail.
I'm kind, pleasant, delightful,
Charming and extremely brave!
I trot very quietly and slowly.
My hooves go *tip-tap! Tip-tap! Tip-tap!*
I'm terrified of the hideous, revolting,
ugly, nasty troll!
Who am I?

Answer: *The first Billy Goat Gruff.*

Freya Lucas (6)

Brownsover Community School, Brownsover

Can You Guess Me?

I am amazingly clever and thoughtful,
only when I want to be!
I wear ragged clothes
and a blue, shiny headband.
I have an unbelievably horrid stepmother!
I have some incredibly short and curly hair.
My hair glistens in the sun.
I have beautiful curls
because I don't touch them.
My hair is midnight-black and shiny.
Who am I?

Answer: Snow White.

Sophie Woolhead (7)
Brownsover Community School, Brownsover

Can You Guess What I Am?

I am really clever,
Handsome and adventurous.
I am helpful, cheeky and naughty.
I am strong, funny and silly.
I am tiny, amazing and adventurous.
I am talented at making tiny things.
I have a green hat.
I make beautiful red shoes
In the middle of the beautiful, dark night.
What am I?

Answer: An elf.

Maya Pawlowska (7)
Brownsover Community School, Brownsover

Try And Guess Me!

I was locked in a tower, but now I'm not.
I am talented because I paint on walls.
I have a rusty turquoise frying pan
Because if a stranger comes in I hit them!
My favourite colour is purple
And that's why I wear a purple bowed dress.
I have long, beautiful golden hair.
Who am I?

Answer: Rapunzel.

Karina Zsofia Pallosi (7)
Brownsover Community School, Brownsover

Can You Guess Who I Am?

I am extremely tiny and short,
So you might not see me.
I'm cheeky, cunning and mischievous.
I run quickly from danger!
I have a toffee top hat.
I am brown, delicious and crunchy.
My favourite saying is,
"Run, run as fast as you can!"
Who am I?

Answer: The Gingerbread Man.

Caleb Nolan

Brownsover Community School, Brownsover

Can You Guess Me?

I am smart, confident and speedy.
I like to speedily run fast, but I am careful.
I have no family or friends
which makes me extremely lonely!
I am cheeky!
I am unbelievable, sweet,
gingery and delicious.
I like to run as fast as I can!
Who am I?

Answer: The Gingerbread Man.

Charlie Ryan Whittle (7)
Brownsover Community School, Brownsover

Can You Solve My Riddle?

I have a beautiful, bright, spotty T-shirt.
I have glittery, shiny tights.
I behave good and bad
And I didn't listen to my mum.
I am a girl.
I am not a very good girl!
I have shiny, golden hair.
I love porridge, but I eat the wrong bowl.
Who am I?

Answer: Goldilocks

Adám Sólyom (7)
Brownsover Community School, Brownsover

Who Am I?

I am male.
I am very scary.
I'm revolting and horrible.
I have massive yellow fangs
Sticking out my mouth.
I have dark green skin.
I live under a smelly, stinky bridge.
I have eaten all of the three
Billy Goats Gruff.
Who am I?

Answer: The Troll.

David Farnworth (7)

Brownsover Community School, Brownsover

Can You Guess Me Today?

I am beautiful, extremely kind and cheerful.
I like to be happy,
Unbelievably wonderful and magnificent.
I am an incredibly shiny and cool princess.
I have been poisoned by a witch.
I have been sleeping for a hundred years.
Who am I?

Answer: Sleeping Beauty.

Elliana To (6)
Brownsover Community School, Brownsover

Can You Guess Who I Am?

I am old but I am only five years old!
I have a big grey fur.
I am brave and very strong.
I have two giant horns.
I am grumpy and very wise.
I am fast and rich.
I have nice pink nails.

Who am I?

Answer: One of the three Billy Goats Gruff.

Riley Evan Sherlock (6)

Brownsover Community School, Brownsover

Can You Solve My Riddle?

I am a bold, smart and clever girl.
I skip happily through the gloomy forest.
I am the bravest girl ever!
I like to carry in my tiny basket
some yummy treats for my granny.
I wore a shiny ruby-red cape.
Who am I?

Answer: Little Red Riding Hood.

Juee Deshpande
Brownsover Community School, Brownsover

Can You Guess Who I Am?

I am joyful because I escaped from a house.
I am fast but I am clumsy.
I outran a granny!
My buttons were white icing
and I have crunchy legs.
I am quite rude
because I jumped out of an oven.
Who am I?

Answer: *The Gingerbread Man.*

Joseph Ngan (6)
Brownsover Community School, Brownsover

Can You Guess Who I Am?

I have black stripes and I am cute.
I have a sharp sword.
I have sharp claws.
I am smart because I can hide anywhere!
I jumped on a tree and spied on the mouse.
I have orange eyes.
I wear boots.
Who am I?

Answer: Puss in Boots.

Liam Finch (7)
Brownsover Community School, Brownsover

Can You Guess Who I Am?

I am chubby, helpful and adorable.
I have a beautiful, huge flower
in my spiky hand.
I have a long, straight tail.
I have fluffy whiskers.
I have a pink and bright nose.
I have a walking stick.
Who am I?

Answer: The Town Mouse.

Emilia Rose Jones (6)
Brownsover Community School, Brownsover

Who Am I?

I am a young girl.
I am a beautiful princess.
I have shimmering gold hair,
I'm very friendly, helpful and joyful too.
I pricked my finger on a spinning wheel.
I fell asleep for a hundred years.
Who am I?

Answer: Sleeping Beauty.

Luiza Maria Kremska (6)
Brownsover Community School, Brownsover

Can You Guess Who I Am?

I have a red coat with a hood.
I have a wonderful, beautiful red dress.
I have short hair that is brown.
I have a brown bag
With chocolate biscuits and cake inside.
I go to visit my grandma.
Who am I?

Answer: *Little Red Riding Hood.*

Sinead Gilbert (7)

Brownsover Community School, Brownsover

Who Am I?

I have long hair.
I am a beautiful girl.
My favourite colour is red.
I am really adventurous and brave.
I don't get scared easily.
I can visit my grandma.
I live in the woods.
Who am I?

Answer: Little Red Riding Hood.

Juliet Wood
Brownsover Community School, Brownsover

Can You Guess Who I Am?

I am a young man.
I am small, and I have a huge smile.
I have three shiny buttons
on my brown chest.
I'm cheeky, funny and cheerful.
I don't like foxes.
I can run fast.
Who am I?

Answer: *The Gingerbread Man.*

Jude Lee
Brownsover Community School, Brownsover

Who Am I?

I am a man.
I am the ugliest man ever!
I am a funny little man.
I am foolish.
I am mean.
I am unkind.
I have a funny name!
I want the girl's jewellery.
Who am I?

Answer: Rumpelstiltskin.

H J Borloch (6)
Brownsover Community School, Brownsover

Can You Guess Who I Am?

I am extremely bright orange.
I am incredibly thoughtful, kind and brave.
I have a green hat my master gave me.
I wear brown boots.
I am mischievous and cheeky.
Who am I?

Answer: Puss in Boots.

Jacob Colledge (7)
Brownsover Community School, Brownsover

Can You Guess Who I Am?

I am disgusting, hungry and here.
I have sharp horns.
I am selfish and mean.
I live under a bridge.
I'm fat, horrible and mean.
Who am I?

Answer: The Troll.

Jack Raine (7)
Brownsover Community School, Brownsover

Can You Guess What I Am?

I have two pointy ears.
I have a long, sharp nose.
I am crafty, clever and creative!
I am extremely hard-working.
I make shoes.
What am I?

Answer: An elf.

Elsie-Mai Nguyen (6)
Brownsover Community School, Brownsover

Fun Winter Days

I am something you will find when it is cold.
Often in a garden full of white, fluffy snow.
The stones from the garden will make up
my coat.
Twigs and leaves will complete me.
Don't forget a carrot for my nose.
But do try to keep me out of the sun
or I will melt.
What am I?

Answer: A snowman.

Ruby Jasmine Allen (6)
Goodyers End Primary School, Bedworth

Glorious Weather

I have the hottest weather.
I am a season.
It's not likely to rain.
It's not good weather to go running.
I can sometimes hurt people.
If I do hurt somebody, I am sorry.
I can be a girl's name.
What am I?

Answer: Summer.

Enva White (7)
Goodyers End Primary School, Bedworth

Animal

I am super hairy like feathers.
I have sharp teeth.
I make a roaring sound.
I am furry around my head.
I am scary.
I live in a zoo or jungle.
I have four feet.
What am I?

Answer: A lion.

Zenia Habibani (6)
Goodyers End Primary School, Bedworth

Pink

She is pink.
She wears a crown.
But she never has a frown.
She is always happy.
She never wears a nappy.
She has a brother and also a mother.
Who is she?

Answer: Peppa Pig.

Lia Hull (6)
Goodyers End Primary School, Bedworth

My Favourite Friend

I am round.
I get kicked.
I get muddy.
I fall into a net.
I am big.
I am different colours.
What am I?

Answer: A football.

Archie Aubrey Gilchrist (5)
Goodyers End Primary School, Bedworth

Magical, Colourful And Big

I have four legs.
I am colourful.
I am magical.
I can fly.
I have big wings.
I have a horn.
What am I?

Answer: A unicorn.

Roisin Duffy (6)
Goodyers End Primary School, Bedworth

The Sunny Holiday

I am warm, sunny and fun.
I am splashing.
I am bright.
I am soft beneath your feet.
What am I?

Answer: Summer.

Abby McKinlay (6)
Goodyers End Primary School, Bedworth

Man's Best Friend

I have four legs.
I am a pet.
I like bones.
I don't like cats.
I can bark.
What am I?

Answer: A dog.

Ethan Lewis (6)
Goodyers End Primary School, Bedworth

Spell Caster!

She has a pointy hat like a mountain.
She has a pointy nose like a banana.
She is waving a wand in the sky.
She has a cauldron to make spells.
Her red spot is like a dragon.
Her broom is as long as a stick.
What is she?

Answer: A witch.

Alfie Grimshaw (6)
Hillmorton Primary School, Hillmorton

Spell Caster!

She makes poisonous potions.
She waves a sparkly wand.
She rides around on a wicked broom.
She has a nose as long as a carrot.
She has a long black hat like a mountain.
Her cackle fills the sky.
What is she?

Answer: A witch.

Amira Yadav (6)
Hillmorton Primary School, Hillmorton

Spell Caster

She has a pointed hat
As pointed as a mountain.
She makes poisonous potions.
She has a sparkly wand.
She has a pet cat as keen as can be.
She has a thin broomstick.
She has a bow.
What is she?

Answer: A witch.

Evelyn Taylor (5)
Hillmorton Primary School, Hillmorton

Magic Wand!

She has a pointed nose with a spot.
She is smelly.
Her friends are helping her too and she is helping them.
On her head, she has a pointed hat.
She has a broom.
She cackles loudly
What is she?

Answer: A witch.

Emilia Butler (6)
Hillmorton Primary School, Hillmorton

Spell Caster

She has a hat like a mountain.
She holds a wand in her hand.
She has a broom.
She makes potions in her cauldron.
Her nose is as long as a carrot.
Her broom is as long as a log.
What is she?

Answer: A witch.

Emily Harper (5)
Hillmorton Primary School, Hillmorton

Spell Caster!

She has a very pointy nose.
She has a very big cauldron.
She has a very magical wand.
She has a super flying broom.
She has a sharp hat!
She has a big wart on her nose!
What is she?

Answer: A witch.

Millie Clarke (5)
Hillmorton Primary School, Hillmorton

Spell Caster

She wears a silly dress.
She makes glittery potions.
Her wand is as sparkly as the sun.
Her nose is like a banana.
Her broom is as long as a carrot.
She has a long hat.
What is she?

Answer: A witch.

Eleanor Basnett (5)
Hillmorton Primary School, Hillmorton

Poof, Spells

She has a pointed broom like a headband.
She has a shiny wand.
She has a pointed hat like a knife.
She has a long nose like a banana.
She has a big spotty bow.
What is she?

Answer: A witch.

Amelia Moon (5)
Hillmorton Primary School, Hillmorton

Spell Caster!

She wears a pointed hat like a knife.
She has a sparkly wand.
She has a long nose.
She makes a cauldron.
She has a spotty skirt.
She wears a spotty bow.
What is she?

Answer: A witch.

Miriam Jouni (6)
Hillmorton Primary School, Hillmorton

Spell Caster

She has a magic broomstick.
She does magic.
She has a magic cauldron.
She has a hat as long as a log.
She has a magical wand.
She casts spells
What is she?

Answer: A witch.

William Harker (6)
Hillmorton Primary School, Hillmorton

Spell Caster!

She makes horrible potions.
She has a really pointy hat.
She has a cauldron.
She has a yellow, sparkly wand.
Her cackles fill the sky.
What is she?

Answer: A witch.

Hope Poole (5)
Hillmorton Primary School, Hillmorton

Long Speller!

She eats worms
On her head she wears a hat.
She has a nose longer than a mountain.
She has a fussy cat.
What is she?

Answer: A witch.

Reece Robson (5)
Hillmorton Primary School, Hillmorton

Singing

I can sing as loud as I can.
I have a partner that stands next to me.
I can let go or stay on my sight.
I do not have legs.
I go on a stage when I am ready.
I am black and never white.
I never get stolen, only when I am hidden.
I get shiny in the dark.
I stay in a *keep out* room.
I never get left outside.
Sometimes, I am an outside singer.
What am I?

Answer: A shiny microphone.

Nyah Habinshuti (7)
St Francis Catholic Primary School, Bedworth

My Best Friend

He likes to go for walks.
His favourite food is chicken.
He's only one foot tall.
He likes to bark at the birds.
He doesn't like to share his bed.
Small, cute, screwed up black face.
He comes from China!
He rhymes with the word 'jug',
But doesn't look like a slug.
Who is he?

Answer: Alfie the pug.

Jem Luca Raggett (7)
St Francis Catholic Primary School, Bedworth

Roary From India

I am sly in the jungle.
I like to come out at night.
I am snoozing on hot summer days.
I have an enormous curly tail.
I devour my prey.
My teeth are as sharp as scissors.
I am extremely fast, unlike a snail.
I am the bright colour of orange
With stripes of the night.
What am I?

Answer: A tiger.

Olivia Simmons (6)
St Francis Catholic Primary School, Bedworth

Find Me

I am something everyone owns.
You find me in most places especially
homes.
I come in a lot of different styles
and colours.
I cover a lot of playful miles.
I am sometimes misplaced
and cannot be found.
When I'm tossed in a basket,
not tied or bound.
What am I?

Answer: A pair of socks.

Oliver Gilbey (6)

St Francis Catholic Primary School, Bedworth

The Fairway

My clubs are not for joining.
I have lots of tees, but no cups or saucers.
I have lots of swings, but no slides.
You can play in the sand
Without a bucket and spade.
My birdies don't have any feathers!
Of course, you can play a round
On my favourite colour green.
What am I?

Answer: Golf.

James Charlton-Horrillo (6)
St Francis Catholic Primary School, Bedworth

I Love Reading

I am thin, but I'm also thick.
Don't put me down, you might miss a trick.
I am made from paper and cardboard.
You won't get tired or bored.
I am colourful and bright.
You can only see me in the light.
I can be happy or sad,
Or very scary and mad.
What am I?

Answer: A book.

Holly Garratt (7)
St Francis Catholic Primary School, Bedworth

Extinct

I lived a long, long time ago,
But parts of me are still on show.
I can be as big as a house
Or small like a mouse.
I can be gentle and friendly,
But most of us are really scary.
I like a juicy plant to munch,
But most of us would eat you for our lunch.
What am I?

Answer: A dinosaur.

Ethan Coyle (7)

St Francis Catholic Primary School, Bedworth

Laika's Kennel

I have fins that glide me on my way.
My engines are loud and fiery.
I fly fast, I fly high.
I always point towards the sky.
I have windows and doors,
But I'm not a house.
Where I'm going, there is no knowing.
What am I?

Answer: A rocket.

Dominic Charlton-Horrillo (6)
St Francis Catholic Primary School, Bedworth

What Am I?

I am fluffy.
I can be any colour.
I have dark ears.
I like hay.
I don't have sharp teeth.
I have a soft tail which is very long.
I go *clip-clop, clip-clop* when I walk and run.
What am I?

Answer: A horse.

Mailey Grace Golby (7)
St Francis Catholic Primary School, Bedworth

Best Friend

I follow you all day.
At night, I go away.
I come in different sizes.
At different times of the day.
You can make me into puppets.
But never throw me away.
I am always feeling grey.
What am I?

Answer: A shadow.

Isabella Campbell (7)
St Francis Catholic Primary School, Bedworth

Under The Sea

I live under the sea.
I can breathe on land.
I have suckers to taste and smell.
I feel very soft.
I have no bones.
I won't bite.
I have nine brains.
I have eight arms.
What am I?

Answer: An octopus.

Miley Green (6)
St Francis Catholic Primary School, Bedworth

Cheeky Chappy

I eat bananas.
Sometimes, I live in a zoo.
I have a long tail.
I like to climb and swing from tree to tree.
I like to go *ohh, ohh, ahh, ahh*.
I am cheeky.
I am cute.
What am I?

Answer: A monkey.

Lily Jade Spencer (7)
St Francis Catholic Primary School, Bedworth

Cake Party

I have icing.
I have cherries on the icing.
I have candles on the top.
I am soft.
I am edible.
I am brilliant to eat.
I go to everyone's birthday party.
What am I?

Answer: A birthday cake.

Leon Max Sumner (6)
St Francis Catholic Primary School, Bedworth

The King Of The Trees

I'm furry and brown.
I hang around.
The treetops are my home.
This is where I roam.
I eat bananas and fruit.
Sometimes, I swing around
And play on the ground.
What am I?

Answer: A monkey.

Lydia Crowley (6)
St Francis Catholic Primary School, Bedworth

My Feathered Friend

I am brightly coloured.
I live in a tropical forest.
My beak is strong and curved.
I can pick up my food with my feet.
I am very intelligent.
I can copy what you say.
What am I?

Answer: A parrot.

Sarah Murphy (6)
St Francis Catholic Primary School, Bedworth

Slither And Slide

I am green.
I lurk in the water
Of swamps and marshlands.
I am found in South America.
I am a reptile.
I have scaly skin.
I eat from above and below.
What am I?

Answer: A green anaconda.

Scarlett Dadley (6)
St Francis Catholic Primary School, Bedworth

Under The Sea

I live underwater.
I sometimes live in coral.
I have lots of names.
Sometimes, I am very famous.
Often people eat me.
I am in some great tales.
What am I?

Answer: A fish.

Joshua McAnespie (7)
St Francis Catholic Primary School, Bedworth

Pixel Puzzle Poem

I love to gobble fruit.
I am thirty-eight years old.
I avoid ghosts.
I live in an arcade.
I have a big mouth, but no eyes.
I am banana yellow.
Who am I?

Answer: Pac-Man.

Thomas Dixon (7)
St Francis Catholic Primary School, Bedworth

Man's Best Friend

When the postman comes, I run to the door!
I like to chase around after my tail.
I have four legs.
I have a wagging tail.
I bark a lot.
Who am I?

Answer: Bessie, my dog.

Freddie Bayliss (6)
St Francis Catholic Primary School, Bedworth

Squeak, Squeak

I am small and cute.
I am a good pet.
I am born with all my teeth and fur.
I make squeaking noises.
My name is a country and an animal.
What am I?

Answer: A guinea pig.

Cian Kincaid (7)
St Francis Catholic Primary School, Bedworth

Super Styles

I come in different styles.
I can help you walk for miles.
I come in a pair.
I am something you wear.
With heels I am glam.
What am I?

Answer: A pair of shoes.

Oscar Leszek Wilk (6)
St Francis Catholic Primary School, Bedworth

Winter Wonderland

I am as cold as ice.
I can turn you into an ice sculpture
with my coldness.
I am soft and defrosting.
I can make a car get stuck.
What am I?

Answer: Winter.

Olivia Katherine Jones (7)
St Francis Catholic Primary School, Bedworth

My Pet

I am fluffy.
I sleep in a basket.
I like to be stroked.
I go outside a lot.
I have a tail.
I say *miaow*.
What am I?

Answer: A cat.

Louisa Thorpe (7)
St Francis Catholic Primary School, Bedworth

Healthy

I am in the fridge.
I am a vegetable.
I am green.
I am bumpy like popcorn.
I can be in a soup.
I am healthy.
What am I?

Answer: Broccoli.

Iga Laura Surys (7)
St Francis Catholic Primary School, Bedworth

Wild

I have fur.
I am small.
I can be fast at running.
I can be prey for some animals.
What am I?

Answer: A sheep.

Liam Gilbody (6)
St Francis Catholic Primary School, Bedworth

Fluffy Creatures

If you see me, I will hide.
You may find me in the snow.
I am camouflaged,
But I don't live in the jungle.
I have fluffy wings and a fluffy body.
I have a little orangy beak.
My wings are quite flappy and wacky.
Normally I fly silently,
So no one knows I'm here.
You will find me up or below in the snow.
I can beat a wolf when I am flying.
I fly as fast as lightning.
I pounce on the mice greedily.
I am a meat eater.
What am I?

Answer: A snowy owl.

Florence Isla Forgan (6)
St Mary's Catholic Primary School, Southam

The Little Muncher

I am a mammal.
I can run as fast as lightning!
I have eyes on the side of my head.
I am as big as your hand.
My tail is like a pompom!
I have soft, bushy fur that is grey.
I have big back legs.
I eat raisins, nuts, berries and greens.
I make burrows in mud or hay.
I blend into rocks.
I can scamper into little places.
I have long ears.
I like to hop really high.
I live in a hutch and in a house.
I am a pet.
What am I?

Answer: A bunny.

Lydia Reeves (7)
St Mary's Catholic Primary School, Southam

An Arctic Burrower

I am very small.
I am furry.
I have sharp teeth
With incisors that grow rapidly.
You can't see me
Because I scurry as fast as lightning.
Sometimes, I like to hide.
I like to roll in the snow.
I like to make dens.
I am a little muncher.
Arctic foxes eat me.
I have a little tail.
I live in the Arctic.
I have stripes on me.
What am I?

Answer: A lemming.

Elena Raiseborough (7)

St Mary's Catholic Primary School, Southam

A Squeezer

I live in a jungle.
I sometimes live in the zoo.
I squeeze things to death!
I hide in the grass.
My tail moves when I slide in the grass.
I am big and thick.
I slide my body on the ground.
I am spotty.
My skin is green.
I eat anything for my dinner.
I move slowly.
I am a meat eater.
What am I?

Answer: A boa constrictor.

Gwendolyn Bosworth (6)
St Mary's Catholic Primary School, Southam

Furry But Friendly

I have whiskers,
I pounce on my prey,
I eat mice,
I am a mammal.
Sometimes, I have kittens.
I have soft skin.
Sometimes, I am brown.
I have four paws.
I can sniff my prey from far away.
I have sharp claws.
What am I?

Answer: A pet cat.

Sophie Bartlett (6)
St Mary's Catholic Primary School, Southam

Arctic Swimmer

I am a mammal.
I live in the Arctic.
I like eating fish.
I like to swim with my mother.
My fur is white and fluffy.
Pesky penguins are trying to eat me!
What am I?

Answer: A seal pup.

Carolina Ferreira Jorge (7)
St Mary's Catholic Primary School, Southam

The High Hopper

Sometimes white, but I am grey.
I am fluffy.
I have a bushy tail.
I have long teeth.
I hop high.
I have very long ears.
Sometimes, I eat lettuce.
What am I?

Answer: A rabbit.

Maya Gulliver (7)
St Mary's Catholic Primary School, Southam

An Upside-Down Riddle

I sleep upside down.
I sleep in a tree.
I use my ears to see.
I come out at night.
I hang upside down.
Some suck your blood.
I can eat fruit.
What am I?

Answer: A bat.

Olivia Mulkeirins (6)
St Mary's Catholic Primary School, Southam

A Mean Animal

You have to be careful
Because I can bite you!
I live in the forest.
I like chasing animals.
I hunt in the forest.
I love eating meat.
What am I?

Answer: A bear.

Ada Sztuka (6)
St Mary's Catholic Primary School, Southam

A Tall Riddle

I have four legs.
I have a swishy tail.
I am tall and strong.
I can carry people.
I crunch carrots.
I can race.
What am I?

Answer: A horse.

Lyekka Mae Robinson (5)
St Mary's Catholic Primary School, Southam

The Jungle

I pounce on my prey!
I try to eat every day.
In the jungle I play.
I am stripy.
In the jungle I like to climb trees.
What am I?

Answer: A tiger.

Jacob Leslie Holden (6)
St Mary's Catholic Primary School, Southam

A Fire Riddle

I am scary.
I am huge.
I eat meat.
I have a tail and lots of scales.
I live in castles.
I breathe fire.
What am I?

Answer: A dragon.

Logan Crowther (6)
St Mary's Catholic Primary School, Southam

A Fluffy Riddle

I have long whiskers.
I sleep on your bed, with my soft head.
I am covered in fur.
If you stroke me, I will purr!
What am I?

Answer: A cat.

Sofia Reeves (5)
St Mary's Catholic Primary School, Southam

The Laziest Animal

I live in the damp Amazon Rainforest.
I like climbing tall trees.
I am a slow creature.
I like eating, soft, crunchy leaves.
My scariest predator is a jaguar.
I go to the toilet once a week.
I have two hands and two feet.
I'm very lazy to others.
I can't be a pet.
You can have more of us.
We've got very gripping hands.
What am I?

Answer: A sloth.

Rosa Sinclair (7)
The Revel CE Primary School, Monks Kirby

The Animal

I have fluffy, white, soft fur.
I eat orange, yucky, stinking fish.
I have pointy, long nails and they are yellow.
I waddle on ice with my friends.
I live in the Arctic in the freezing cold.
I flap my wings but cannot fly.
What am I?

Answer: A penguin.

Krystal Brook Hipwell (6)
The Revel CE Primary School, Monks Kirby

My Favourite Pet

I am a pet.
I have an owner.
I come in most colours.
I live in a cosy hut.
I am fluffy.
I have whiskers.
I eat fish.
I drink milk.
I purr.
I *miaow!*
When I was a baby, I was a kitten.
What am I?

Answer: A cat.

Katherine Harrison (6)
The Revel CE Primary School, Monks Kirby

Pant, Pant, What Was That?

I am a pet.
I eat meat and treats.
I can be any size you like
It depends on what you choose.
I can run, walk, jump and even stand up!
I can live in any house.
I can bark and woof.
I was a puppy when I was a baby.
What am I?

Answer: A dog.

Philippa Bennett (7)
The Revel CE Primary School, Monks Kirby

Furry And Hairy

I have very sharp claws.
My ears are furry.
I like to eat yummy blue fish.
When I am cross, I roar like a lion.
I have green gloomy eyes.
My teeth are tall and yellow.
I live in a cave.
What am I?

Answer: A bear.

Annie Zhou (5)
The Revel CE Primary School, Monks Kirby

Jungle Cat

I like to eat meat.
I have sharp, pointy claws.
My teeth are big, white and sharp.
I am furry like a dog.
My fur is orange and stripy.
I have a long tail.
I live in the jungle.
What am I?

Answer: A tiger.

Charlie Main (7)
The Revel CE Primary School, Monks Kirby

My Favourite Animal

I am a pet.
I am very furry.
I have a tail.
I can come in lots of colours.
I eat meat and bones.
I bark very loud.
I can live in houses.
When I was a baby, I was a puppy.
What am I?

Answer: A dog.

Poppy Rose Lindstrom (7)
The Revel CE Primary School, Monks Kirby

What Am I?

I live in a rainforest.
I like to go swimming to relax.
I have long teeth.
I am very big.
I am the king of the river.
I eat fish and other animals.
I fight others.
What am I?

Answer: A hippopotamus.

Lauchlan MacKenzie (6)
The Revel CE Primary School, Monks Kirby

Miaow

I am a pet.
I have whiskers.
I have a tail.
I have pointy eyes.
I live in houses.
I eat fish and meat.
I like chasing mice.
When I was a baby, I was called a kitten.
What am I?

Answer: A cat.

Sasha Pickering (6)
The Revel CE Primary School, Monks Kirby

What Am I?

I am fat.
I eat grass
My wheel is amazing.
I eat nuts.
I have brown and white patches
On my back.
I am scared of you.
I have black eyes.
I have pink ears.
What am I?

Answer: A hamster.

Phoebe Bloor (5)
The Revel CE Primary School, Monks Kirby

What Am I?

I love to hunt in the long grass.
I look like I have spots.
I am yellow.
My tongue is pink.
I hear well.
I bite people.
I swallow people.
I live in the jungle.
What am I?

Answer: A cheetah.

Eloise Smith (6)

The Revel CE Primary School, Monks Kirby

The Flying Creature

I move in the sky.
I can be red or blue.
Sometimes, you see me on a branch.
You see it on the forest floor.
I eat lots of bugs.
I am medium.
I live on the floor.
What am I?

Answer: A butterfly.

Lydia Wallwin (6)
The Revel CE Primary School, Monks Kirby

Purrfect

I am a pet.
I am good at climbing fences.
I am good at eating meat.
I have four legs.
When I am happy, you hear me purr.
When I was a baby, I was a kitten.
What am I?

Answer: A cat.

Adam Lea (6)
The Revel CE Primary School, Monks Kirby

What Am I?

I have a long tail.
I have four different feet.
I have lots of spots.
I have black, beady eyes to find my prey.
I have sharp ears.
I have a weird nose.
What am I?

Answer: A leopard.

Vinnie Humphreys (5)
The Revel CE Primary School, Monks Kirby

What Am I?

I have sharp teeth.
My tail is very long.
I have a very short tongue.
I have a spotty body.
I live in the rainforest.
I am the fastest thing ever born.
What am I?

Answer: A cheetah.

James Burton (5)
The Revel CE Primary School, Monks Kirby

The Flying Beast

I have a very sharp beak.
I have a pair of wings.
I have a spotty tail.
I have stripy and spotty wings.
I have two feet.
I live in a tree in a nest.
What am I?

Answer: An eagle.

Myles Wright (5)
The Revel CE Primary School, Monks Kirby

Tiny Creature

I live in a large group.
I eat fish.
I slide on my belly.
I like swimming.
I have a pointy beak.
I live in the Arctic
I like standing on ice.
What am I?

Answer: A penguin.

Oliver Mann (6)
The Revel CE Primary School, Monks Kirby

What Am I?

I swing from branch to branch.
I eat lovely yellow bananas.
I say *ooh, ooh, ahh, ahh!*
I live in the Amazon Rainforest.
I can be big or small.
What am I?

Answer: A monkey.

Isabel Rees (6)
The Revel CE Primary School, Monks Kirby

What Am I?

I have fluffy fur.
My tail is fluffy.
I am spotty.
My feet are called paws.
My paws are sharp.
My nose is wet.
I wag my tail when I am happy.
What am I?

Answer: A dog.

Sinead Naylor (6)
The Revel CE Primary School, Monks Kirby

Whiskers

I am a pet.
I eat fish.
I have four legs.
I like to play with cotton balls.
I have a long tail.
I come in different colours.
I love to play.
What am I?

Answer: A cat.

Eira Pitham (6)
The Revel CE Primary School, Monks Kirby

The Spots

I have four legs.
I have a long tail.
I have some yellow fur.
I have some whiskers.
I have some yellow fur on my ears.
I have spots.
What am I?

Answer: A leopard.

Jacob Farr (6)
The Revel CE Primary School, Monks Kirby

Cotton Wool

I am a pet.
I'm fluffy.
I have four legs.
I come in different colours with patches.
I have whiskers.
I jump around in the grass.
What am I?

Answer: A rabbit.

Amelia Price (7)
The Revel CE Primary School, Monks Kirby

What Am I?

I have yellow teeth.
My breath smells bad.
I have gold hair.
My paws are black.
I eat my prey.
I eat animals.
I have black eyes.
What am I?

Answer: A lion.

Adley Ball (5)
The Revel CE Primary School, Monks Kirby

What Am I?

I climb up trees
And swing from branch to branch.
I like to eat bananas.
Some of us are very clever.
I am strong.
I climb up trees.
What am I?

Answer: A monkey.

Millie Jones (7)
The Revel CE Primary School, Monks Kirby

The Mixed-Up Riddle

I have four legs.
I am white.
I eat fish.
I live in a cold place.
I stumble through the snow.
I was a cub when I was a baby!
What am I?

Answer: A polar bear.

Lara Grieves-Smith (6)
The Revel CE Primary School, Monks Kirby

Rainforest Creature

I live in a rainforest.
I eat insects and bugs.
I have a scaly body.
I throw spiders when I am attacked!
I am a type of lizard.
What am I?

Answer: A Tongo lizard.

Arthur Wang (7)

The Revel CE Primary School, Monks Kirby

What Am I?

I am white and black.
I can live in any place.
I am very furry.
I can be big or small.
I can run very fast.
I am not that tough!
What am I?

Answer: A puppy.

Maddie Jankowski (6)
The Revel CE Primary School, Monks Kirby

The Hopping Thing

I like to eat crunchy carrots.
I have floppy ears.
I live in a hutch.
I like to eat lettuce.
My skin is fluffy.
I hop and jump
What am I?

Answer: A rabbit.

Lottie-Anne Cardwell (5)
The Revel CE Primary School, Monks Kirby

What Am I?

I like to eat flies.
I am very hairy.
I am quite small.
I live all around the world.
I move slowly.
I'm not that strong.
What am I?

Answer: A spider.

Stanley Smith (6)
The Revel CE Primary School, Monks Kirby

The Jumping Animal

I have a long tail.
I have long ears.
I have sharp teeth.
I have yellow teeth.
I have a small mouth.
I have a strong kick.
What am I?

Answer: A kangaroo.

Taylor Smith (5)

The Revel CE Primary School, Monks Kirby

What Am I?

I walk in the snow.
I have white fur.
My habitat is in the North Pole.
I eat lots of fish.
I like to go swimming in the sea.
What am I?

Answer: A polar bear.

Alfie Dennis Wright (5)
The Revel CE Primary School, Monks Kirby

Roaring King

I have a fluffy mane.
I have sharp claws.
I have sharp teeth.
I have beady eyes.
I have a tail.
I am the king of the jungle.
What am I?

Answer: A lion.

Evie Sawyer (6)
The Revel CE Primary School, Monks Kirby

Bubble, Bubble

I can be a pet.
I eat things that are smaller than myself.
I have scales.
I live in water.
I have no legs.
I have a tail.
What am I?

Answer: A fish.

Tilda Passemard (7)
The Revel CE Primary School, Monks Kirby

Sea Creature

I come in lots of forms.
I have no legs.
I eat any kind of meat.
I don't make a sound.
I am grey.
I live in the sea.
What am I?

Answer: A shark.

Edward Barrett-Leafe (7)
The Revel CE Primary School, Monks Kirby

What Am I?

I can run fast.
I'm very spotty.
I live in the jungle and the wild.
I am nearly the fastest land animal.
I have a tail.
What am I?

Answer: A cheetah.

Dominic Poole (6)
The Revel CE Primary School, Monks Kirby

What Am I?

I am a medium-sized.
I have colourful wings.
I eat seeds and nuts.
I have red, blue, or yellow coloured feathers.
I can fly.
What am I?

Answer: A parrot.

Layla Jade Huddlestone (7)
The Revel CE Primary School, Monks Kirby

What Am I?

I spin a lot of webs.
I have eight legs.
I live in many places.
I eat insects.
I am very small.
I am black and red.
What am I?

Answer: A spider.

Lily Grace Elliot (7)
The Revel CE Primary School, Monks Kirby

What Am I?

I am small.
I have got whiskers.
I say *miaow, miaow*.
I've got sharp nails.
I am very strong
I go outside.
What am I?

Answer: A cat.

Gia Murphy (6)
The Revel CE Primary School, Monks Kirby

What Am I?

I live in the sea.
I have eight tentacles.
I don't like to be on land.
I don't like sharks.
I begin with an O.
What am I?

Answer: An octopus.

Charlie Johnson (7)
The Revel CE Primary School, Monks Kirby

Fast Cat

I have a long tail.
I am a type of cat.
I eat meat.
I am in a pack
I have sharp teeth.
I am the king of the jungle.
What am I?

Answer: A lion.

Elsie Sorren Gleed (5)
The Revel CE Primary School, Monks Kirby

What Am I?

I have a wet nose.
I have two flappy ears.
I eat vegetables.
I have sharp teeth.
I will give you a lick to say hello.
What am I?

Answer: A rabbit.

Darcy Victoria Forinton (6)

The Revel CE Primary School, Monks Kirby

What Am I?

I am big.
I live on the forest floor.
I live in Africa.
I bend to drink water.
I eat leaves.
I move slowly.
What am I?

Answer: A giraffe.

Chloe Isobel Porcas (6)
The Revel CE Primary School, Monks Kirby

What Am I?

I have red, yellow and black feathers.
I have a very strong beak.
I eat nuts and fruit.
I live among the canopy layer.
What am I?

Answer: A parrot.

Edward Town (5)
The Revel CE Primary School, Monks Kirby

What Am I?

I live in the canopy layer in the rainforest.
I am thin.
I am short.
I move quietly.
I hiss.
I am quite sly.
What am I?

Answer: A snake.

Ethan William Richardson (7)
The Revel CE Primary School, Monks Kirby

What Am I?

I live in the rainforest.
I can be blue, yellow and other colours.
I like bathing in the river.
I hide in the trees.
What am I?

Answer: A parrot.

Douglas George Harrison (7)
The Revel CE Primary School, Monks Kirby

What Am I?

I am fluffy.
I eat meat.
I have four legs.
I am different colours.
I have whiskers.
I *miaow* loudly.
What am I?

Answer: A cat.

Leo Hunt (6)
The Revel CE Primary School, Monks Kirby

The Adventure

I have a sharp beak.
My skin is fluffy.
I catch my prey with my beady eyes.
I sometimes poop on people's heads.
What am I?

Answer: An eagle.

Harris Leech (5)
The Revel CE Primary School, Monks Kirby

What Am I?

I have a trunk.
I drink water.
I am big.
I am grey.
I can blow out water from my trunk.
I am strong.
What am I?

Answer: An elephant.

Autumn Rose Morris (6)
The Revel CE Primary School, Monks Kirby

What Am I?

I am a pet.
I have a long tail.
I have a long nose.
I have four legs.
When I am angry, I bark!
I am fast.
What am I?

Answer: A dog.

Leeson Lee Tolin (6)
The Revel CE Primary School, Monks Kirby

What Am I?

I have big, long arms.
I have a long tail.
My teeth are yellow.
I love to swing in the trees.
I eat leaves.
What am I?

Answer: A monkey.

James Thomas Dew (6)
The Revel CE Primary School, Monks Kirby

Twitch, Twitch

I am a pet.
I have four legs.
I am very furry.
I am white.
I have whiskers.
I love being played with!
What am I?

Answer: A bunny.

Keira Pargetter (7)
The Revel CE Primary School, Monks Kirby

What Am I?

I like water.
I drink water and suck it up.
I have a dry and smooth tongue.
I have a trunk.
I am huge.
What am I?

Answer: An elephant.

Ella Louise Irons (7)
The Revel CE Primary School, Monks Kirby

Tiny

I am small.
I have six legs.
I am black.
I live in the jungle.
I carry a leaf.
There are lots of me.
What am I?

Answer: An ant.

Bradley Mackley (7)
The Revel CE Primary School, Monks Kirby

A Swimming Animal

I have sharp teeth.
I am colourful.
I swim underwater.
I am spotty.
I have fins.
I live in the sea.
What am I?

Answer: A fish.

Elsie May Ascroft (6)

The Revel CE Primary School, Monks Kirby

What Am I?

I am a pet.
I live in a cage.
I eat meat.
I have fur.
My sound is a squeak.
I have whiskers.
What am I?

Answer: A hamster.

Emily Carol Green (6)
The Revel CE Primary School, Monks Kirby

Flutter, Flutter

Sometimes it flies in the sky.
It sleeps on the grass or in trees.
When it was little, it was cute.
What is it?

Answer: A butterfly.

Maisy Mia Masterson (7)
The Revel CE Primary School, Monks Kirby

What Am I?

I have black fur.
I eat fish.
I have an owner.
When I am a baby, I am tiny!
I play with string.
What am I?

Answer: A cat.

Alfie Green (6)
The Revel CE Primary School, Monks Kirby

Roaring Beast

I have stripes all around me.
My teeth are sharp.
I am scary.
I eat meat.
My eyes are yellow.
What am I?

Answer: A tiger.

Ryan James Fox (6)
The Revel CE Primary School, Monks Kirby

What Am I?

I am purple.
I live in water.
I can spray ink.
I can be quite big.
I have eight legs.
What am I?

Answer: An octopus.

Reuben Oliver Wells (5)
The Revel CE Primary School, Monks Kirby

What Am I?

I am strong.
I am small.
I am grey.
I am rare.
I have spots.
I am black and grey.
What am I?

Answer: A lizard.

Lydia Tomlin (6)
The Revel CE Primary School, Monks Kirby

What Am I?

I have sharp teeth.
I am colourful.
I swim in the sea.
I have fins.
I live in the water.
What am I?

Answer: A fish.

April Steele (5)
The Revel CE Primary School, Monks Kirby

What Am I?

I eat meat.
I can have black and brown stripes.
I have sharp claws.
I am quite scary.
What am I?

Answer: A tiger.

Amelie Pickering (6)

The Revel CE Primary School, Monks Kirby

What Am I?

I have four legs.
I eat fish and tuna.
I love mice.
When I was little I was a kitten.
What am I?

Answer: A cat.

Nanci Fellows (7)
The Revel CE Primary School, Monks Kirby

It Has Got A Small Tail

I swim in the sea.
I have sharp teeth.
I am mean.
What am I?

Answer: A shark.

Elizabeth Barnett (5)
The Revel CE Primary School, Monks Kirby

What Am I?

I am big.
I am black and white.
I run fast.
What am I?

Answer: A zebra.

Taylah Bottomley (7)
The Revel CE Primary School, Monks Kirby

The Ferocious But Lovely Mythical Beast

Surprisingly, I hatch from a stripy black egg.
With my giant nose,
I sniff out new villages to burn down.
Sometimes, when I am hungry,
I eat two thousand burgers in a minute.
When I am grumpy,
I give a loud, deafening roar.
With my soft wings,
I soar through the night sky.
Knights are my worst enemy.
I like chewy meat.
If you look close,
You will see my bumpy scales!
When I am happy, I give a chirp.
What am I?

Answer: A dragon.

William Allan (7)
Welford-On-Avon Primary School, Welford On Avon

The Flaming Riddles With Burning Water

Fiercely, I whizz out of my gloomy,
golden, stripy egg.
I soar through the water and the clouds,
splitting them in half.
Then, I hit the ground,
and use my plasma blast
to blow the trees up!
When I am angry,
I shoot deafening noise blasts
and make people deaf.
When they are deaf, they fall down
and I will jump on them and I roast them.
I sleep in the caves in the mountains.
I sleep for twenty-four hours
and wake up early in the morning.
My teeth are so pointy,
they can slice a rock in half.

If you look carefully,
you will see me at midnight
in my shiny, black scales.
What am I?

Answer: A dragon.

Harry Millwood (7)
Welford-On-Avon Primary School, Welford On Avon

The Dark Wizard's Riddle

Noisily, I hatch out of my gold, spotty egg
Yawning, when it is morning!
Sometimes, I fly in the night
Because I want my breakfast.
Fiercely, I grab a child
With my poisonous fangs
And gobble them up!
Peacefully, I live in places
Where nobody goes because they are scary!
All night I fly and all day I sleep
Because I don't want to be seen!
When I sleep, I sometimes dream
About my family and friends.
What am I?

Answer: A dragon.

Benji Fernandez (7)
Welford-On-Avon Primary School, Welford On Avon

The Big, Scary Creature

I leap out of a big, powerful blue egg.
With my beautiful long wings.
When I am angry,
I give a loud booming roar.
If you look carefully, I have bumpy scales.
With my enormous shiny talons and jaws,
I cause pain.
Sometimes, I can eat a knight
In his shiny armour.
We are threatening creatures
And we distress damsels
We burn down every city we see.
Watch out! I breathe flaming hot fire.
What am I?

Answer: A dragon.

Luke Mulliner (7)
Welford-On-Avon Primary School, Welford On Avon

The Fierce, Evil, Mythical Riddle

Fiercely, I fly smoothly out
Of a beautiful egg.
With my zigzag wings,
I dash out of the village.
Then, I swoop and fly slowly.
Also, I like pouncing on evil humans.
Sometimes, I gallop quickly into a cave.
If you look carefully,
You can see my scaly dark red back.
When I am angry, I go and kill knights!
I am mythical.
Watch out! I will eat you!
No one has ever killed us.
What am I?

Answer: A dragon.

Abigail Twigg (7)
Welford-On-Avon Primary School, Welford On Avon

The Fire-Breathing Lizard

Quickly, I rush out of a beautiful,
golden-blue, dotted egg.
With enormous red nostrils.
I am fierce like a lion.
With my big, banging wings,
I can knock you down.
If you come too close, I will eat you up.
Sometimes, I can get angry
if you feed me the wrong food.
Watch out! I have a wide, gaping jaw.
As I swoop into the forest,
I see a tasty treat.
What am I?

Answer: A dragon.

Olivia Flack (7)
Welford-On-Avon Primary School, Welford On Avon

The Fierce Fire-Breathing Creature

Shockingly, I jump out
Of a sparkly golden egg.
Carefully, I leap into the sky and fly down.
When I am angry,
I use my teeth to crunch houses.
When I am grumpy,
I stomp through the villages.
When I am sad, my tears create a stream.
When I am feeling fierce,
I gobble up people.
Sometimes, I open my sharp jaws wide
And eat!
What am I?

Answer: A dragon.

Katie Potter (6)
Welford-On-Avon Primary School, Welford On Avon

The Fierce, Scary Riddle

When I am young, I'm very big.
Sometimes, if you look closely
You can see my sharp, pointy horns!
Quietly, I zoom out of a giant, scary egg.
If you come too close, I'll eat you up!
Watch me fight fiercely
With other enormous creatures.
On my back, I have lots of scales.
When I am angry,
I give a loud, frightening roar.
What am I?

Answer: A dragon.

Oscar Farnell (6)
Welford-On-Avon Primary School, Welford On Avon

Fierce, Green Giant

I'm slow like a slow snake that is green.
I fly in the air really fast.
I have red lava cheeks.
The spikes on my back are razor-sharp.
My jaws are like a crocodile.
Also, I slither like a snake.
My legs are as big as a tree.
When I get seen, I hide!
Watch out! I grip on rocks.
When I'm happy, I don't play.
What am I?

Answer: A dragon.

Aiden Kesic (6)
Welford-On-Avon Primary School, Welford On Avon

The Scary, Lovely Creature

Slowly, I pop out of a blue, pink
And magical egg.
With my wings I swoop and fly
Quickly through the huge rainbow sky!
When I am angry,
I leap about in my dark grey cave.
If you stare properly,
I have silver and bronze scales!
With my jaws and claws, I cause pain.
Sometimes, I eat a knights head in one go!
What am I?

Answer: A dragon.

Daisy Unsworth (7)
Welford-On-Avon Primary School, Welford On Avon

Fancy Fur

I live in the wavy grass,
When I am angry, I growl.
Watch out! I am sneaky.
Sometimes, I scratch you.
If you give me meat, I will eat it!
You will see me in the jungle.
If you dare to, hear me growl!
My fur is fluffy and spotty.
What am I?

Answer: A cheetah.

Emily McCarthy (6)

Welford-On-Avon Primary School, Welford On Avon

The Horrifying Beast That Is Feared

Crazily, I burst out of a shiny blue egg.
I am the beast that is feared
Through the land.
I sit on the land, I sit on rooftops.
My wings are old and tattered.
My wings are humongous.
You may see a glint of my shiny scales.
What am I?

Answer: A legendary dragon.

Ben George Alderman (6)
Welford-On-Avon Primary School, Welford On Avon

The Gigantic, Scary Creature

Loudly, I pop out of a scary green egg.
With my wings,
I soar through the night chasing the moon.
When I am angry,
I smash windows with a crash!
I have a scaly long tail.
My neck is very long.
I breathe fire.
What am I?

Answer: A dragon.

Dylan Warren (7)
Welford-On-Avon Primary School, Welford On Avon

Fast Charger

Watch out I might eat you.
If you look carefully, I have shiny teeth!
Sometimes, I hide under the water.
I am a fast charger, faster than you!
If you think I am slow, you are wrong!
My colour is grey.
What am I?

Answer: A hippopotamus.

Sam Bright (5)
Welford-On-Avon Primary School, Welford On Avon

King Of The Listeners

Watch out I can scratch you.
I can bite you with my little teeth.
I come from a really hot place.
If you stroke me, I would feel soft.
When I was a baby, I drank milk!
I have a little tail.
What am I?

Answer: A meerkat.

Ines Aughey (6)

Welford-On-Avon Primary School, Welford On Avon

Woof, Woof, Big Barker

Watch out! I can bite you really badly
And all you can see is blood.
I can jump very high,
I can wag my tail very fast.
If I see a cat, I will chase it.
I will go in a muddy puddle.
What am I?

Answer: A dog.

Elizabeth Davies (5)
Welford-On-Avon Primary School, Welford On Avon

Slippery Slider

If you look carefully, I have scales!
I can creep up on people.
Watch out! I may give you a poisonous bite!
I am a reptile.
I don't have feet.
I don't have a neck.
What am I?

Answer: A snake.

Bethany Hills (5)
Welford-On-Avon Primary School, Welford On Avon

Slow Traveller

I don't live in England.
I'm very slow.
I live in Africa.
When I am hungry I eat leaves for tea.
I am small but big too.
My name gives you a clue
What am I?

Answer: A giant African snail.

Pixie-Blue Purtill (6)
Welford-On-Avon Primary School, Welford On Avon

Scary Pounce

With my roar, I scare people.
Watch out, I can gobble you up.
Sometimes, I eat meat.
Sometimes, I am in a tree.
It's dinner time for me.
I want something right now.
What am I?

Answer: A bear.

Tom Yates (5)
Welford-On-Avon Primary School, Welford On Avon

Tree Climber

Watch out! I have sharp claws.
Sometimes, I camouflage
In the brown leaves.
With my claws, I can swing on a tree.
When I move, I am very slow.
I like climbing trees.
What am I?

Answer: A sloth.

Archie Eaton (6)
Welford-On-Avon Primary School, Welford On Avon

A Furry Milker

When I get frustrated, I will scratch you.
I am fluffy.
Watch out! I will bite you.
I have little fangs.
If I want to, I can purr.
I am nice to cuddle.
What am I?

Answer: A kitten.

Ava Scott (6)
Welford-On-Avon Primary School, Welford On Avon

The Female Mummy

I am extremely fierce.
From a hot country, I come from.
Watch out, I eat meat.
I always have sharp claws.
I would go under a tree.
I like to bite.
What am I?

Answer: A tiger.

Jo Kowal (5)
Welford-On-Avon Primary School, Welford On Avon

Est.1991

YOUNG WRITERS INFORMATION

We hope you have enjoyed reading this book – and that you will continue to in the coming years.

If you're a young writer who enjoys reading and creative writing, or the parent of an enthusiastic poet or story writer, do visit our website **www.youngwriters.co.uk**. Here you will find free competitions, workshops and games, as well as recommended reads, a poetry glossary and our blog.

If you would like to order further copies of this book, or any of our other titles, then please give us a call or visit **www.youngwriters.co.uk**.

Young Writers
Remus House
Coltsfoot Drive
Peterborough
PE2 9BF
(01733) 890066
info@youngwriters.co.uk